AIN'T NO MOUNTAIN HIGH ENOUGH

Words and Music by
NICKOLAS ASHFORD and VALERIE SIMPSON

Fast Rock Beat

Lis-ten__ ba - by, ain't no mount-ain high, ain't no val - ley low, ain't no riv - er

wide e-nough; ba - by if you need me call__ me no mat-ter where you are, no mat-ter__ how

__ far; just call my__ name;__ I'll be there in a hur - ry;__ you don't have to wor-

2   I set you free
    I told you you could always count on me
    From that day on, I made a vow
    I'll be there when you want me
    Some way, some how
    'Cause baby there (Chorus)

3   My love is alive
    Way down in my heart
    Although we are miles apart
    If you ever need a helping hand
    I'll be there on the double
    As fast as I can
    Don't you know that there (Chorus)

APACHE

By JERRY LORDAN

BOOM BANG-A-BANG

Words by MICHAEL JULIEN
Music by ALAN MOORHOUSE

Bright Waltz

Come

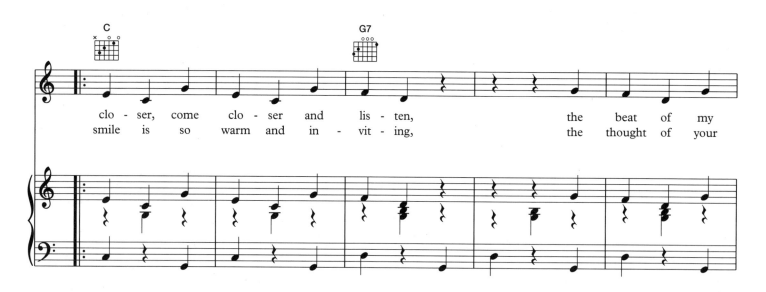

clo - ser, come clo - ser and lis - ten, the beat of my
smile is so warm and in - vit - ing, the thought of your

heart keeps on miss - in', I no - tice it most when we're
kiss is ex - cit - ing, so hold me and don't keep me

BLACK IS BLACK

Words and Music by STEVE WADEY,
TONY HAYES and M GRAINGER

BLUE VELVET

Words and Music by
BERNIE WAYNE and LEE MORRIS

BYE BYE BABY (BABY GOODBYE)

Words and Music by
BOB CREWE and BOBBY GAUDIO

BREAKING UP IS HARD TO DO

Words and Music by NEIL SEDAKA
and HOWARD GREENFIELD

You tell me that you're leav-in', I can't be-lieve it's true!

Girl, there's just no liv-in' with-out_____ you. Don't take your_

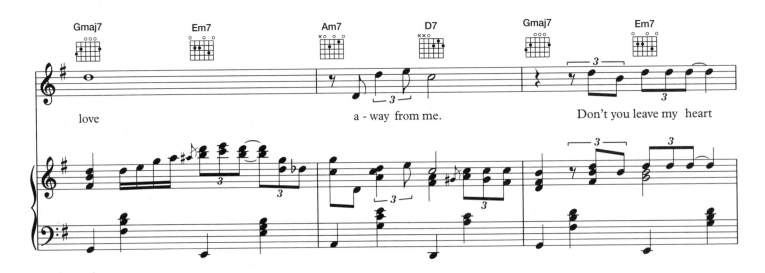

love a - way from me. Don't you leave my heart

C'MON EVERYBODY

Words and Music by
EDDIE COCHRAN and JERRY CAPEHART

Been a - do - in' my home - work all week long, now the
When you hear that mu - sic your feet won't sit still. If your
There'll be no____ more mov - ies for a week or two; No more

house is emp - ty, the folks are gone. Oo, oo!
bro - ther won't, then your sis - ter will. Oo, oo! c'm - on, ev - 'ry - bo - dy!
run - ning a - round with the us - ual crew. Who cares.

2. Well, my
3. Well, we'll

CRYING IN THE RAIN

Words and Music by
CAROLE KING and HOWARD GREENFIELD

1. I'll ne - ver let you see___ the way my bro-ken heart is hurt - in' me.___
2. If I wait for clou-dy skies, you won't know the rain from the tears in my eyes.

I've got my pride and I know how to hide all my sor - row and pain,
You'll ne-ver know that I still love you. So, though the heart-aches re - main,

I'll do my cry-ing in the

rain.

Rain-drops fall-in' from hea-ven could

DAYS OF WINE AND ROSES

Words by JOHNNY MERCER
Music by HENRY MANCINI

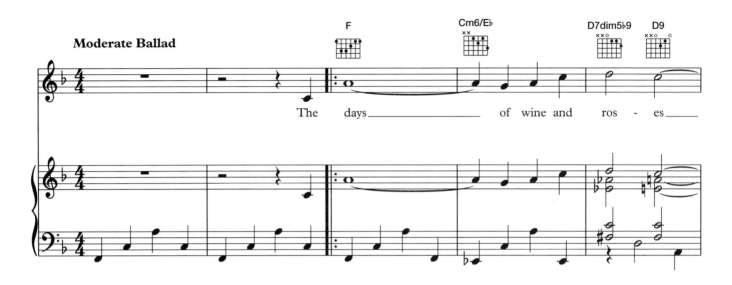

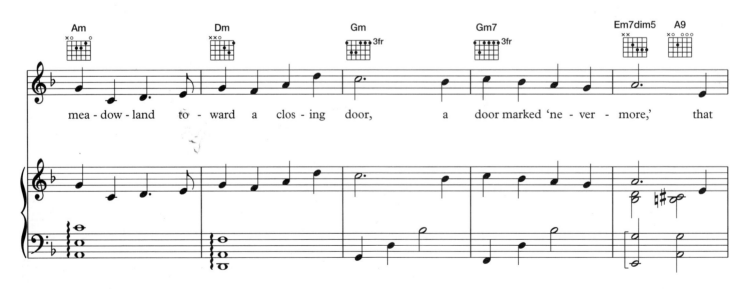

DANCING IN THE STREET

Words and Music by WILLIAM STEVENSON, MARVIN GAYE
and IVY JO HUNTER

Moderate

Call - ing out__ a - round__ the world, are you rea - dy for a brand new beat?
in - vi - ta - tion a - cross the na - tion, a chance for folks to meet.

__ Sum-mer's here__ and the time is right__ for danc - ing in the street.
__ There'll be laugh -ing, sing-ing and mu - sic swing-ing danc - ing in the street.

__ They're danc-ing in Chi - ca - go,__ down in New Or - leans,
__ Phil - a - el-phia, P. A., Bal - ti-more and D. C. Now

grab a girl, __ ev - 'ry - where a - round __ the world. They'll be danc - ing,

they're danc-ing in the street, (danc-ing in the street). This is an __ way down in L. A.

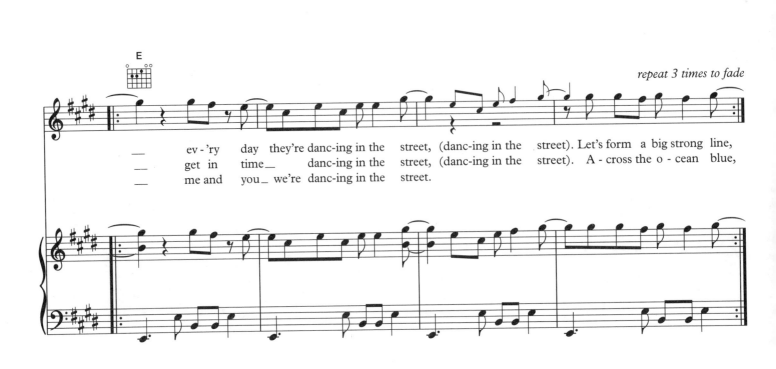

repeat 3 times to fade

__ ev - 'ry day they're danc-ing in the street, (danc-ing in the street). Let's form a big strong line,

__ get in time __ danc-ing in the street, (danc-ing in the street). A - cross the o - cean blue,

__ me and you __ we're danc-ing in the street.

DAYDREAM BELIEVER

Words and Music by JOHN STEWART

DOWNTOWN

Words and Music by TONY HATCH

Medium Rock

1. When you're a-lone___ and life is mak-ing you lone-ly, you can al-ways go___
2. Don't hang a-round and let your prob-lems sur-round you, there are mov-ie shows
3. *(Instrumental to ✱)*

down-town.   When you've got wor-ries, all the noise and the hur-ry seems to
down-town.   May-be you know___ some lit-tle plac-es to go___ to where they

bright - er there,_ you can for - get all your trou - bles, for - get all your cares._ So go
see you there,_ we can for - get all our trou - bles, for - get all our cares._ So go

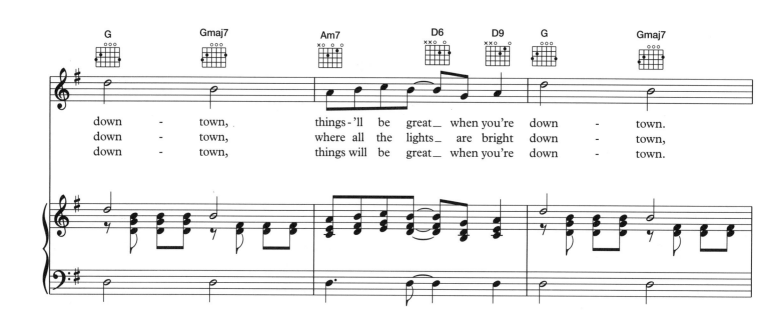

down - town, things -'ll be great_ when you're down - town.
down - town, where all the lights_ are bright down - town,
down - town, things will be great_ when you're down - town.

No fi - ner place,_ for sure, down - town. Ev - 'ry-thing's wait - ing for
wait - ing for you_ to-night down - town. You're gon - na be al - right
Don't wait a min - ute more down - town. Ev - 'ry-thing's wait - ing for

EVERLASTING LOVE

Words and Music by
BUZZ CASON and MACK GAYDEN

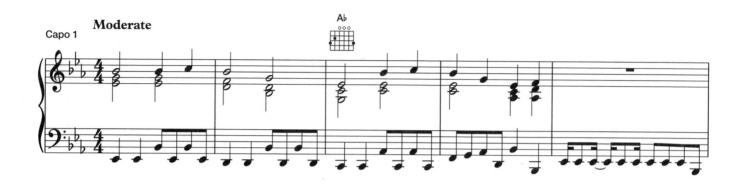

Hearts gone a - stray,   deep in
You won't re - gret   I'll come

hurt   when they   go.   I went a - way   just when
back   beg - gin'   you   won't you for - get?   Wel - come

GOLDFINGER

Words by LESLIE BRICUSSE and ANTHONY NEWLEY
Music by JOHN BARRY

HANDY MAN

Words and Music by
OTIS BLACKWELL and JIMMY JONES

With a beat

Capo 1

Hey girls,__ ga-ther round,____ be-cause of what I'm put-ting down.__

Oh, ba-by, I'm your hand-y man.____

I GOT YOU BABE

Words and Music by SONNY BONO

say we're young and we don't know, won't find out till_____ we
say our love won't pay the rent, be - fore it's earned our mon - ey's al - ways

grow.
spent.

Well I don't know why that's true, 'cause
I guess that's so, we don't have a pot, but at

I'D RATHER GO BLIND

Words and Music by
B FOSTER and E JORDAN

Slow Blues

Some-thing told me _____ it was ov - er _____

when I saw you and him _____ talk - ing. _____

Some-thing deep down _____ in my soul said, 'Cry, boy.' _____

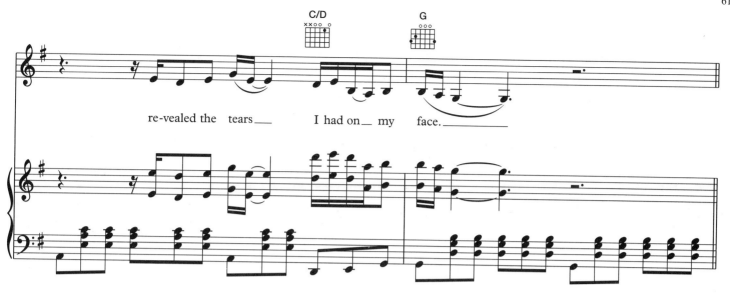

re-vealed the tears___ I had on___ my face._____

I would ra - ther go___ blind, child,_____

repeat to fade

than to see you walk a - way___ from me._____

I HEARD IT THROUGH THE GRAPEVINE

Words and Music by
NORMAN WHITFIELD and BARRETT STRONG

3 People say believe half what you see
Son, and none of what you hear
But I can't help bein' confused
If it's true please tell me dear
Do you plan to let me go
For the other guy you loved before?

WILL YOU LOVE ME TOMORROW?

Words and Music by
GERRY GOFFIN and CAROLE KING

THE WINDMILLS OF YOUR MIND

Words by ALAN and MARILYN BERGMAN
Music by MICHEL LEGRAND

Moderately

Round like a cir-cle in a spi-ral, like a wheel with-in a
Mind! Like a tun-nel that you fol-low to a tun-nel of its

wheel, ne-ver end-ing or be-gin-ning on an ev-er spin-ning reel, like a snow-ball down a
own, down a hol-low to a cav-ern where the sun has ne-ver shone, like a door that keeps re-

YOU'LL NEVER WALK ALONE

Words by OSCAR HAMMERSTEIN II
Music by RICHARD RODGERS